best friends...

understand sharing

by Charles M. Schulz

This edition published by Ravette Publishing 2006.

ISBN 10: 1 84161 258 8
ISBN 13: 978-1-84161-258-4

a friend is

someone who sticks with your team . . . rain or shine

a friend is

someone who remembers to bring the can of balls

a friend is

someone who'll give you a free ride

a friend is

someone who tells you not to worry if you double-fault and lose the winning point

a friend is

someone who appreciates your kind of music

a friend is

someone you
can telephone
after midnight

a friend is

someone who'll go jogging with you at six in the morning

a friend is

someone who'll
let you sulk if
you feel like it

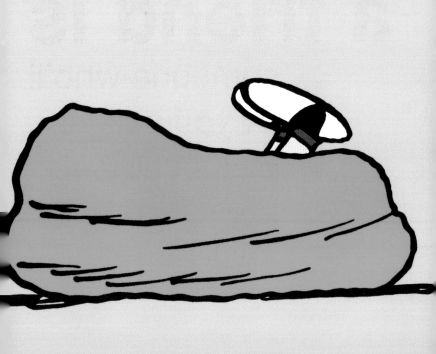

a friend is

someone who'll try to find you when you're lost

a friend is

someone who respects you even if you're not as big as him

a friend is

someone you
can kiss on
the nose

a friend is

someone who doesn't move in on your territory

a friend is

someone who doesn't laugh at you

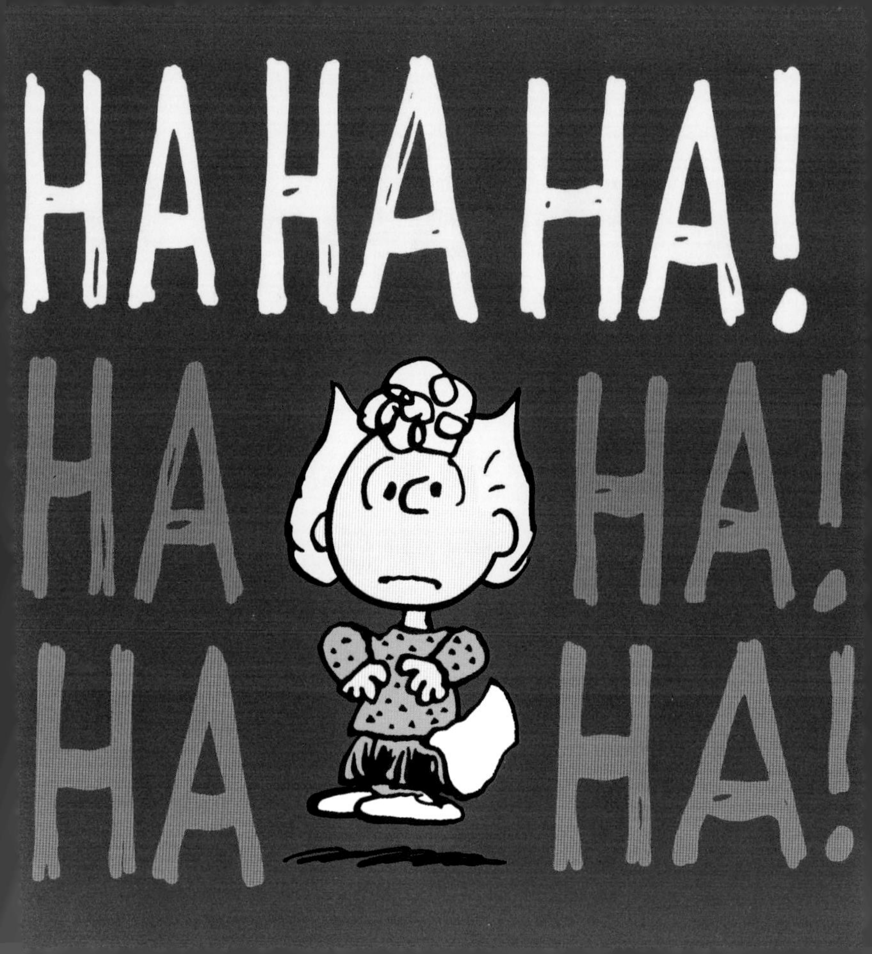
HA HA HA!
HA HA!
HA HA!
HA HA!

a friend is

someone who knows when to keep quiet

a friend is

someone who doesn't tell you anything "for your own good"

a friend is

someone you
can trust

a friend is

someone who gets
a lower grade
than yours and
keeps you from
being the dumbest
in the class

a friend is

someone who doesn't play rough

a friend is

someone who comes to your rescue when you're in a fix

CHOP
CHOP
CHOP
CHOP
CHOP

a friend is

someone who
gives you the
hardback edition
instead of waiting
for the paperback
to come out

a friend is

someone who doesn't make fun of you even when you do dumb things

a friend is

someone who
picks you up
when you're
down

a friend is

someone who
isn't put off
by your crabby
face

a friend is

someone as
sweet and
pretty as
your sister

a friend is

someone who
helps you
to forget your
self-doubts

a friend is

someone who offers to bring dessert when you invite him to dinner

a friend is
someone who
puts you up
for membership
in his club

a friend is

someone who says "my treat"

a friend is

someone who doesn't intrude on your solitude

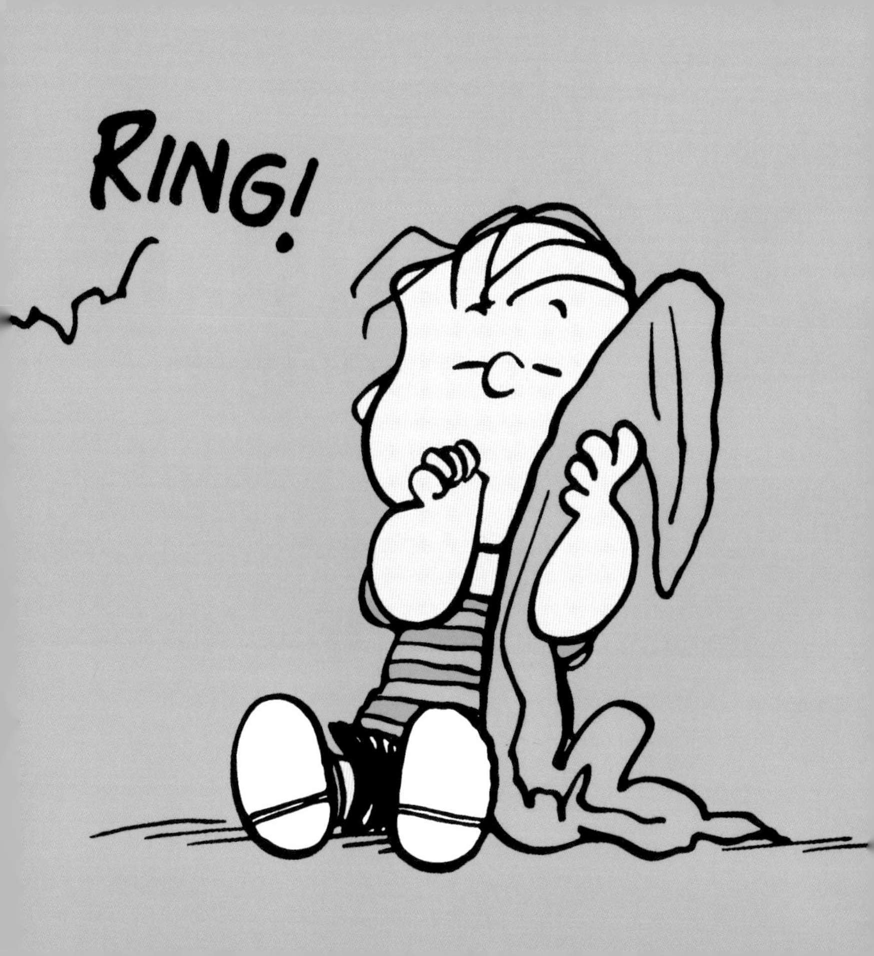
RING!

a friend is

someone you
can count on

Ravette Publishing Ltd
Unit 3, Tristar Centre, Star Road
Partridge Green, West Sussex RH13 8RA
Tel: 01403 711443   Email: ravettepub@aol.com